Paw Paw dedicates
this book to you

ZZ

Written by D.M. Dahman

Illustrated by Caitlin Lothamer & Suzanne Klaehn

# Arrrrr Matey,

this is Captain Jack,

follow me on a letter hunt that will lead you to a treasure chest!

One of my sailors drew up

the _nchor

onto the ship

it almost sank her

Out on the water

the _oat bounced and tossed

when the wind settled down

it sped up a few knots

My mates on the ship are
known as the _rew
some raise the mast
some cook the stew

When the voyage is over we
go get some   _inner
some homemade food sounds
like a winner

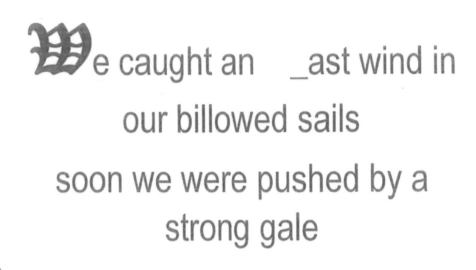

We caught an _ast wind in
our billowed sails

soon we were pushed by a
strong gale

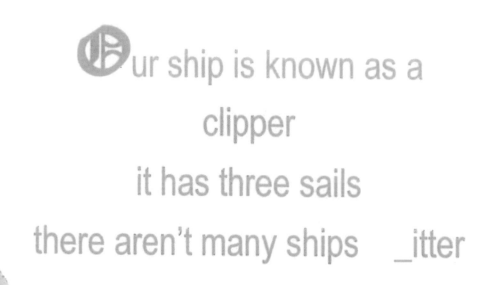

Our ship is known as a
clipper
it has three sails
there aren't many ships    _itter

When the crew wants to eat
they go down to the _alley
the cook is ok but he's not my
Aunt Sally

At least twice a year

we pull into the _arbor climb
in a small boat
and go to the barber

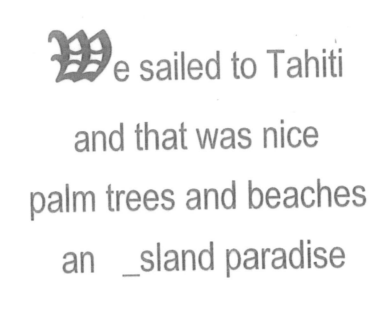

We sailed to Tahiti

and that was nice

palm trees and beaches

an _sland paradise

We have cargo on board

that we ship sea to sea

this is the _ob

we do for a fee

At night it gets dark
but we still need to see
we carry around lanterns filled
with _erosene

We struck some coral then
heard a big crunch
now our boat's been repaired
and we are ready for  _aunch

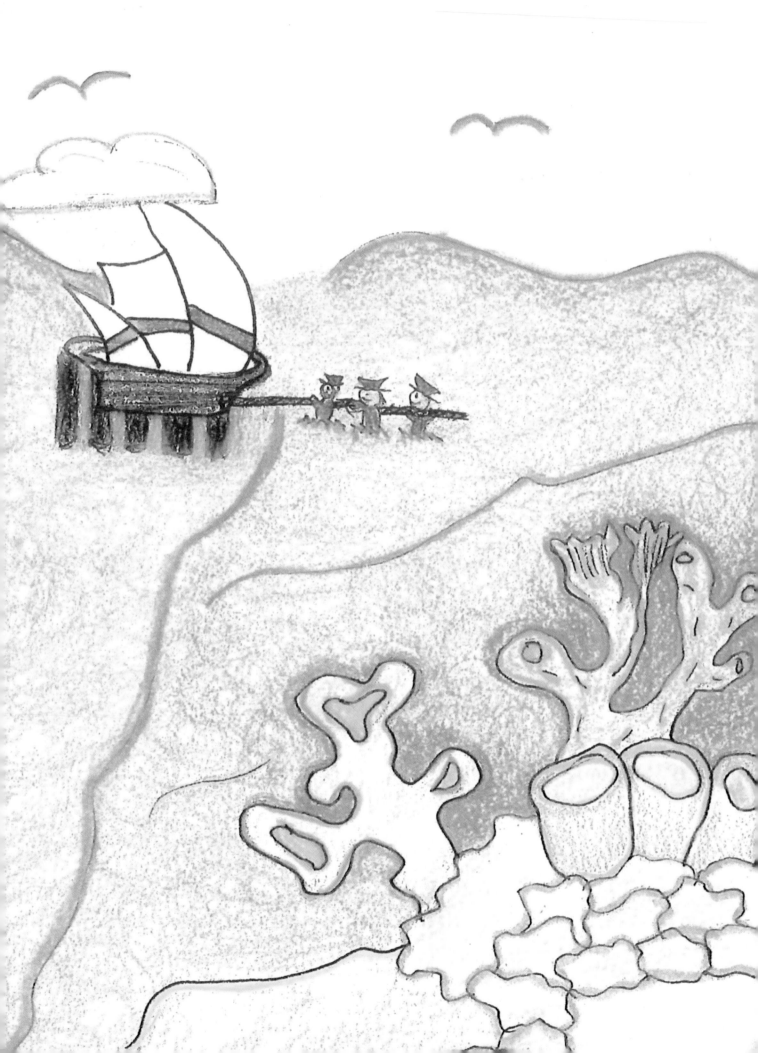

The \_ast is a pole
that supports the sail
some are as long
as a dragon's tail

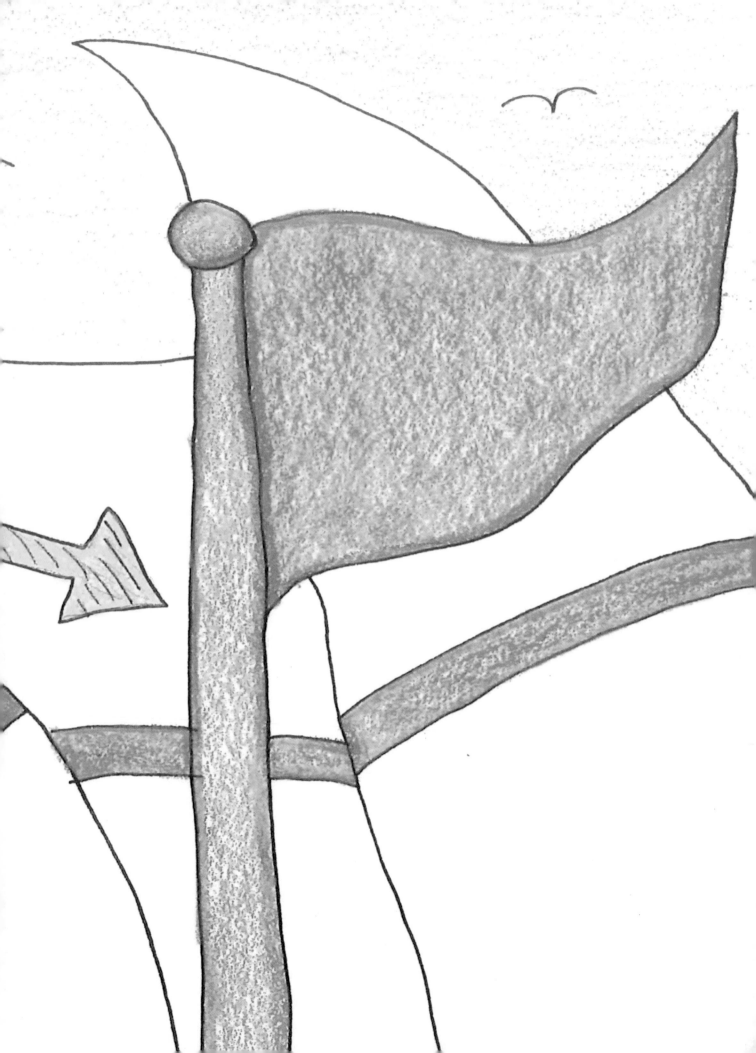

When we _avigate

we follow a course

like pulling the reins

left and right

on a horse

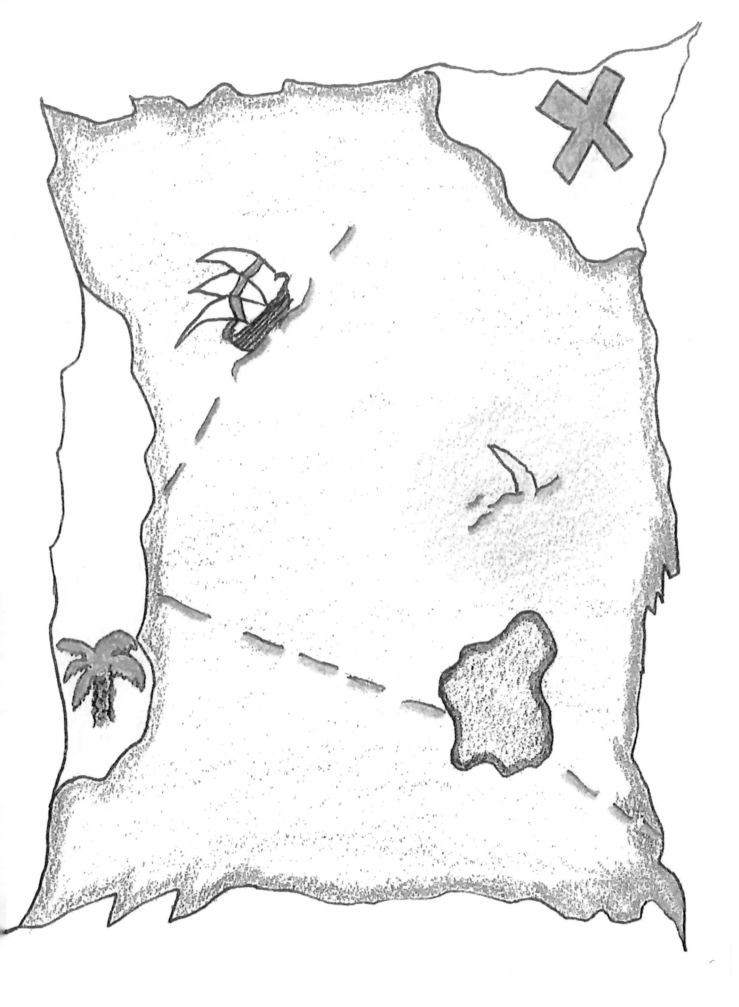

We have _ars for
small boats on the side
we're going to need
them to go for a ride

A _irate is one who robs
and plunders at sea
they take what they want
they get it for free

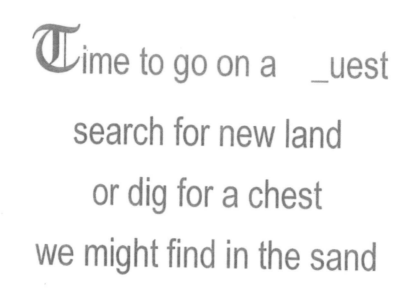

Time to go on a   _uest

search for new land

or dig for a chest

we might find in the sand

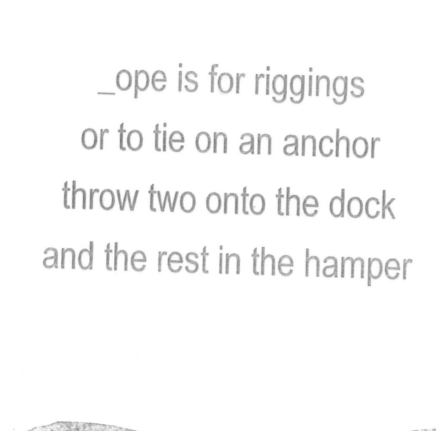

_ope is for riggings

or to tie on an anchor

throw two onto the dock

and the rest in the hamper

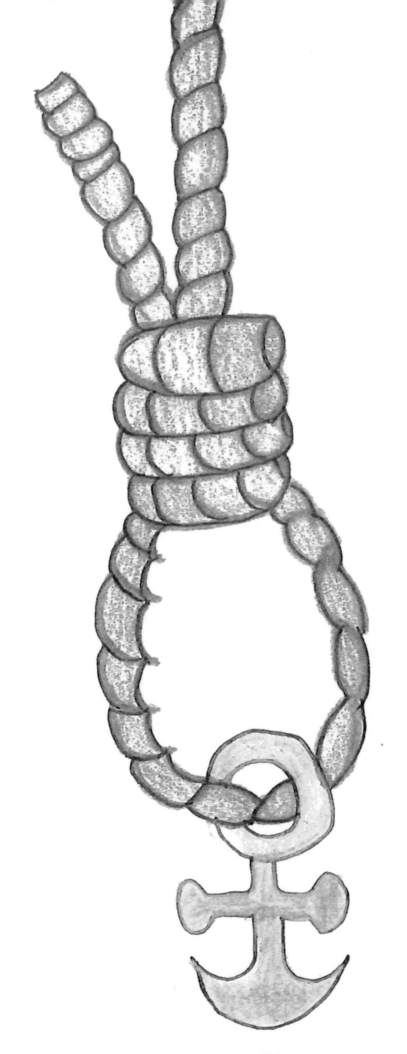

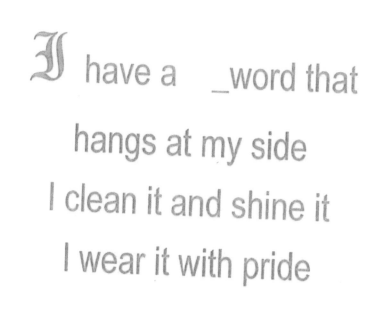

I have a _word that

hangs at my side

I clean it and shine it

I wear it with pride

$\mathfrak{I}$f you're searching for

_reasure that pirates buried

and see skull and cross bones

better leave in a hurry

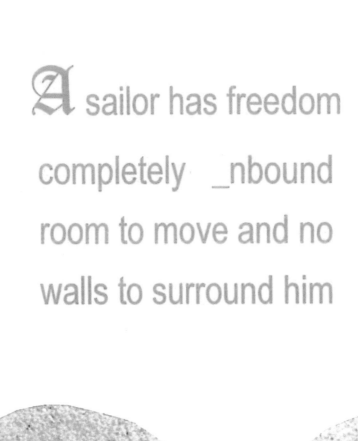

A sailor has freedom
completely _nbound
room to move and no
walls to surround him

Among my garments

I have a leather     _est

it fits quite nicely

on my big hairy chest

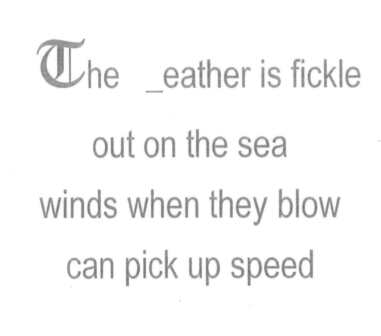

The _eather is fickle

out on the sea

winds when they blow

can pick up speed

_ is the letter
that marks the spot
when looking for
treasure it helps a lot

$\mathfrak{I}$ start  _earning for home

I've been gone for so long

I can't seem to help it

the feeling is strong

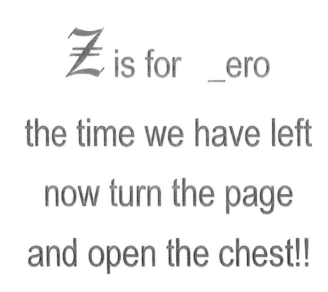 is for _ero

the time we have left
now turn the page
and open the chest!!

Congratulations Matey!!!

You've opened the chest!!!

It's a treasure indeed!!!

You've passed the test!!!

This is a chest that

shouldn't be buried!!!

It contains treasured letters

in the vocabulary!!!